OFF TO THE SUPERMA

The Gang Learn About

BY MARIANNE LEWIS
ILLUSTRATED BY JOE GOODE

Published by MoneySmartWorld Limited.
www.MoneySmartWorld.com
978-09562421-0-5
itish Library Cataloguing in Publication Data. A catalogue record for this book is available from the British Library.

"Come on you two," said Meg's mother, "we have to hurry or we will get stuck in the rush hour traffic!"

Meg and Jasmine climbed into the back of the car excitedly.

They loved going to the shops and today Meg had a list of everything she had been dreaming about all week.

"I want those lovely chocolate bonbons and jammy dodgers," she whispered to Jasmine.

"Oooh! And those sweets with the sherbet in them," she added, her eyes growing big at the thought of them.

"I thought you liked those haribo sweets," said Jasmine laughing at the face Meg was pulling.

"No, I've gone off them," she said.

"Now my favourites are the sherbet ones!"

As they pulled into the car park, they saw Ade, Max and Lily standing at the entrance to the shopping mall.

"What are you doing here?" asked Jasmine, surprised to see her friends.

"Lily and Max's mum said we could ride in her car as long as we behaved," said Ade.

Max and Ade's mums were already inside the Supermarket getting the food shopping for the week.

"We are going downstairs to the sports shop to look at the new football kit that has just come in."

"I like Manchester United's new kit," said Max while Ade said "no, I like Chelsea's! Their colours are cooler."

"Football!" muttered Lily pulling the 'boys will be boys' face she had seen her mother give whenever football was mentioned.

"OK, we'll meet you here in about an hour," they all said to each other and set off to their different shops.

In the supermarket, Meg's mum got out her shopping list and started to fill the trolley.

Meg was impatient and wanted to run on to the biscuits and sweets section, but her mum told her that she and Jasmine must stay with the trolley.

In went the tea bags, sugar, washing powder, vegetables, milk and all sorts, until finally, they came to Meg's 'heaven' – the sweet stuff!

"Now," said Meg's mum, "you can pick two things that you want from this section".

"Only two?" exclaimed Meg "but I want the sherbet and Jammy Dodgers and chocolate bonbons and......"

"Enough of all that!" said her mum, cutting her off in mid sentence. "You can have two types of sweets and that's that."

"No... but mum," said Meg pushing out her lower lip. "No buts, Meg. You just want all this stuff that you don't really need, don't you?" said her mum.

"But I do need them. I can eat them all!" said Meg, looking disappointed.

"Meg, being able to eat all the sweets you want, doesn't make them something you need," replied her mum.

"Mrs Ward."

"Yes, Jasmine," answered Meg's mum.

"What is the difference between the things we need and the things we want?" she asked.

"Well, the things we need are those things that we must have in order to survive. These include items like food, clothes and so on."

"While the things we want are some of the nice things that we like to have.

These are things like sweets, going on holidays and having computer games," answered Meg's mum.

For example, what Meg needs is good food to make her healthy and strong. But, what she wants are loads of sweets and biscuits which are not so good for her, or her teeth if she has too much of them!"

"Ah, I understand," said Jasmine.

"But they taste nice," said Meg trying to reason with her mum.

"Yes of course, they do," said her mum, "but you always have to get the things you need first, and then you can get some of the things that you want with any money that is left over."

"You can't just go out and buy everything that you want. So, let's do it this way, Meg," said her mum, "you can have one pound and fifty pence to spend on your sweets and biscuits."

"But that is the limit, and they have to last you until we come shopping next time. So think before you buy anything, OK?"

"OK!" said Meg, a little glumly, but quite happy to be able to buy what she wanted.

So, she and Jasmine went up and down the aisle looking at the prices.

First, she picked her favourite sherbet sweets, and then went for the biscuits but found that the two came to more than the one pound and fifty pence that her mum had given her.

In the end, she chose a smaller packet of biscuits and the larger packet of sweets, since she knew they would last longer.

Satisfied, they went downstairs to look for the rest of the gang.

"Wow! Look at this new football kit," said Max staring up at the Manchester United kit. "Yes, and look at the new Chelsea kit too!" said Ade excitedly.

"The kids at school will think we are so cool, when they see us in these," said Max.

Just then Max and Lily's mum, along with Ade's mum, came to look for them.

"Why are you all so excited?" asked Max's mum.

"Because they are looking at the new football kits," said Lily with a bored expression on her face.

"Yes, very nice!" said Ade's mum. "Now, let's go in and get your new football kit for the school team."

"But I want the Chelsea kit," said Ade with a voice that was almost a whine.

What you want and what you need are two different things!" she said.

She explained that if they wanted to play for the school team, then they needed the correct uniform and not the first division football kits.

"If the school lets everyone wear whatever they wanted to, how would anyone know who was on which side?" she said.

"I guess you're right", they said together, although they were both disappointed.

"If you want these football kits, then you should save up your pocket money to buy them, or ask for them for your birthdays," said Ade's mum and they brightened up at this.

Both Max and Ade had birthdays within the next couple of months, so it wasn't so long to wait.

"In other words," said Lily, "you have to get what you need first and then if you have enough, or if you can save enough, you can get what you want".

Ade's mum said, "That's exactly right Lily!" giving her a small hug.

They spent almost an hour in the shop trying out the school's football kit until they were satisfied with the result.

Lily was kitted out for her football team too, and she didn't mind that it was in the school colours.

"I'm really not bothered," she explained to the boys, "as long as I can play, then I don't care what I play in!"

When the group and the mums gathered back in the car park, Max's mum listened to Meg's story about wants and needs in the supermarket.

"So, have you all learnt something today?" she asked.

They all echoed "yes," in unison, except Lily. "What about you, Lily?" asked her mum, "You are very quiet."

"Yes," she said, "I've just remembered that I NEED to go home because I WANT to watch my cartoons, but I NEED to get my homework done before Monday!"

Everyone laughed at this and piled into the cars to
go home.

NOW THINK ABOUT THE STORY

1. Which one of Meg's friends went to the supermarket with her?

2. What was Meg planning to buy for herself at the supermarket?

3. Why do you think it is important to get what you 'need' first?

4. How does something you 'want' differ from something you 'need'?

5. Name some things you 'want' but don't necessarily need.

6. How did Meg spend the £1.50 given to her by her mum?

7. Why is it important to budget for your wants and needs?

8. Why do you think we sometimes 'want' something that is not necessary?

9. When you want something (perhaps a new fashionable toy) are you always happy you got it?

10. Do you think Max and Ade will save up to buy their football kits, or ask for it as a birthday present?

PRACTICAL TIPS FOR TEACHING CHILDREN ABOUT WANTS & NEEDS

• Give your child some money (e.g., five pounds or dollars) and let them think about the best way to spend that money on items for the home. You could take them to the supermarket to help them get a realistic idea of what things cost. For example, they could buy 1 box of cereal, 3 tubes of toothpaste or loads of crisps. Help them become a smart consumer by discussing how your family decides on its needs and wants at the supermarket.

• Teach them how friends and TV adverts may influence what they decide to spend their money on.

• Have your child make a list of the things he or she needs or wants and research how much they cost. Give them some pocket money, and/or extra paying jobs to help them earn and save up to buy the items on their list.

• Help them understand that they may not always be able to buy everything on their list, and that making a choice involves giving something up (i.e., the sweet or the chocolates etc)

• Help them create and stick to a budget, in order to teach and support effective money-managing skills.

Note for parents/teachers/guardians: You can download a version of the question sheet, along with suggested answers from the free resource and downloads section at www.MoneySmartWorld.com